Chronic Emotional Fatigue

by

Billie J. Sahley, Ph.D.

In Association With
Katherine M. Birkner, C.R.N.A., Ph.D.

Pain & Stress Therapy Center Publications
San Antonio,Texas
1994

Note to Readers

This material is not intended to replace services of a physician, nor is it meant to encourage diagnosis and treatment of illness, disease or other medical problems by layman. This book should not be regarded as a substitute for professional medical treatment and while every care is taken to ensure the accuracy of the content, the authors and the publisher cannot accept legal responsibility for any problem arising out of experimentation with the methods described. Any application of the recommendations set forth in the following pages is at the reader's discretion and sole risk. If you are under a physician's care for any condition, he or she can advise you whether this is appropriate for you.

This publication has been compiled through research resources at the Pain & Stress Therapy Center in San Antonio, Texas 78229.

Second Edition

Previous Edition, 1992
Printed in the U.S.A.

A Pain & Stress Therapy Center Publication

Additional copies may be ordered from:
Pain & Stress Therapy Center
5282 Medical Drive Suite 160
San Antonio, TX   78229
(210) 614-PAIN

Library of Congress Card No. 92-060781
ISBN 0-9625914-2-4

Contents

Dedicated To

Katherine M. Birkner, R.N., C.R.N.A., Ph.D., who has given the past 10 years of her life to help me reach out to those who suffer and conquer our impossible dream.

Doris Rapp, M.D. whose dedication to healing has given me a constant flow of energy and determination.

And to The Lord for always lighting my path.

Introduction

All too often, when a patient with chronic emotional fatigue goes to a physician to find out what is wrong, the patient will be told that he might have chronic fatigue or he has depression. The reason for this book is to help those who suffer from chronic emotional fatigue understand it. It is not to confuse what you are feeling and why.

Chronic emotional fatigue can and does in many ways mimic chronic fatigue, but that is where it ends. In Harrison's Principles of Internal Medicine, it states fifty to eighty percent of all disease is psychosomatic in nature. That means there is no pathology or disease. This does not mean there is not pain, there is, a lot of it!

The key is that chronic emotional fatigue is stress induced. It results from a traumatic episode or experience that you have no control over, or from an accident of a loved one, divorce or any event that causes prolonged uncertainty and stress. The mind becomes so saturated that the mental stress surfaces in physical symptoms, a little at first, then a constant flow. The immune system breaks down, fatigue sets in as well as depression, fear, anxiety and uncertainty.

To my knowledge, there has not been any other research published on chronic emotional fatigue. This is the first, but I do not feel the last, since this problem is now affecting millions of Americans. I plan to continue my research in this area and to update my findings as information becomes available.

Billie J. Sahley, Ph.D.
Executive Director
Pain & Stress Therapy Center

Recognizing Chronic Emotional Fatigue

If you are one of the millions who suffer chronic emotional fatigue, you will recover from it. Do not get discouraged reading about the symptoms, you will get better. Understanding them is the first step to healing. I doubt those of you who are nervously ill know to what extent fatigue has helped make you ill and has kept you ill. Chronic emotional fatigue acts, not only in very subtle ways, it can come on gradually and insidiously. Few people recognize it or know that many symptoms they dread are no more than the symptoms of constant unrelenting stress that lead to chronic emotional fatigue.

Let me explain how chronic emotional fatigue works and how you can cope with it, even avoid it. When you can do this, you will be well on the way to recovery. Of course, if you are prepared to accept your suffering even without understanding it, it would follow that you would be accepting the effects of fatigue and will not get better.

Understanding what is happening to you is a very powerful weapon. It controls fear and anxiety. The information contained in this book is based on years of patient observations. Chronic emotional fatigue can show itself as a physical fatigue. By that I mean bodily weariness. Or it can surface as anxious fatigue, mental fatigue, and the kind of fatigue that effects the mind. This fatigue seems to rob the sufferer of the will to get better. Ordinary physical fatigue is easy enough to recognize. Fatigue comes to everyone after strenuous exercise, playing tennis, walking five miles. It feels good after a hot bath or hot tub to lie in bed tired, but relaxed, and even enjoy the feeling of aching muscles. But the physical fatigue that comes with anxious fatigue is not enjoyable. It does not come from the extra use of muscles. It comes from the abuse of muscles by subjecting them to the tension that accompanies constant anxiety.

Resting muscles are in the condition called tone. They are firm and ready for action, not limp or flaccid. They are kept in tone by reflex nervous action. You probably know what reflex action is. If I were to tap your knee just below the kneecap, your leg would jerk automatically. That is reflex action. I could make your leg jerk this way all day without it becoming tired. Reflex action is never tiring. So keeping muscles in tone is not tiring. But tension uses nervous energy and it also allows the chemicals of muscular fatigue such as lactic acid to collect. This is why nervously ill people so often complain of aching legs, backs, and necks, even aching arms. This kind of ache is so constant, that if the nervously ill person has to stand, perhaps only for a few minutes, he would look around for some support to lean on or head straight home to bed where he feels safe.

Later, I will explain the nutrient deficiencies that cause restless legs and constant muscle spasms. Chronic emotional fatigue is especially puzzling because the sufferer knows it can strike for no reason. So he is always ready to believe there must be something physically wrong with him. He is the sort of person who lives in the doctor's office having one test after another. He is even more puzzled because he feels almost unable to drag his body out of the bed in the morning. By evening he may not feel so bad. He may even feel like he might be improving. In these moments of relief from suffering, he can sometimes see through the mist and glimpse the possibility of getting better. He holds on to these times. He fears he will lose them. He fears going to bed because he knows from experience that morning will bring the same old churning stomach, same despair, same weary body. It is a tiredness almost beyond tiredness and very depressing.

This is difficult to explain to a family. A patient's husband said to his wife, "You cannot be tired, you have not done anything all day."

She said, "Doctor, I can hardly crawl around and my eyes feel as though they are being dragged out of their sockets. I sit and try to accept. I keep having anxiety attacks. I listen to relaxation tapes, and I try to relax. But my body stays all tied up in spasms something terrible. What am I doing? What's wrong?"

Actually, she was not doing what I had told her. She was neglecting to take the needed nutrients and amino acids, and she was not practicing her deep breathing to relax. She would spend a few minutes trying to relax and then an hour anxiously waiting to see if her body got the message. I told her to begin walking.

Her husband who was listening on the extension phone said, "I have not forced her to do anything."

But if this particular woman were to wait until she felt like walking she would still be waiting. It is difficult for the chronic emotionally ill person to decide about how much work or play she can do without harming herself. She would stand with a paint brush posed wondering, "Should I really be doing this? Would I not get better quicker if I rested? Am I overdoing it?"

The word, *rested*, holds the key to the puzzle. How much does a person with chronic emotional fatigue rest when she sits doing nothing? Very little! Especially if she lies down during the day and tries to sleep. With her head on her pillow, it is almost as if she focuses only on how bad she feels. And there is so much time to concentrate on all the negatives she becomes more anxious and more tense. If she has a problem to worry about, which she always has, by the time she has spent an hour or more concentrating on it, with fear well at work, the problem becomes a major crisis. You can bet it will be health related. She is more exhausted when she gets up than when she first lay down. From then on, she probably will avoid lying down in the daytime. Uncertainty is the only thought!

If you suffer from emotional fatigue, you may well ask, "Well how much can I do?" You can attempt anything you feel up to and want to do. I said attempt because I do not want you to set a high standard of achievement. Be satisfied with what little you can do at first. It is the _attempt_ that matters. I do not mean that you should paint the wall of the house with a paint brush and then rush inside for a soft drink and watch television. I mean at least do some work. But, if necessary, do it at a slow pace. As you become more confident that you do not loose control, you may even become interested in what you are doing. Now is when you can really rest. With interest and confidence aroused, the battle is half over. Confidence and interest are tension's and anxiety's worst enemies, and therefore, the enemy of fatigue. A nervously ill person may only have to move quickly to feel the heart, as one man expressed it, "Pound so hard I felt it in my mouth." This is perhaps one of the fearful experiences in emotional fatigue. The heart may also, as the layman says, skip beats. If you have been examined by a doctor and told that your symptoms are caused by stress and anxiety, and there is nothing wrong with your heart, do not be upset by your heart's objection to work. Just keep on slowly and let your muscles get used to being used slowly and release naturally. Just take one day at time.

Anyone who has been sitting at a desk for months getting little physical exercise will find that his heart will race with little effort, even skip beats. No doctor would suggest that a man should keep sitting at his desk and not get exercise for fear of damaging his heart. Graduated exercise would be the prescription for him, just as it is for the emotionally fatigued person, racing heart or no racing heart. A good massage would help the sore aching muscles and do worlds of good. Lack of confidence has kept so many people wrapped up in fear and anxiety.

Some years ago I persuaded a patient to go swimming. He thought he would get so exhausted that he would not be able to walk the distance to the beach. He managed to, and then stood shivering with anxiety at the edge of the water. He was sure he would have a heart attack when he walked into the water. If he could hardly manage to walk the fifty yards to the beach, how could he find the strength to swim. Finally with the fear, he entered the water, not only fearing the worst, but now prepared for it, muscles tensed. But as he began to swim, the memory of all those other occasions when he swam well brought him a little confidence. For once past memory was his friend, not playing old tapes of fear. After a little while, he struck out into the deep water. He was actually enjoying swimming. I heard no more about the stress and anxiety of walking home.

In one daring exercise that man had gained more confidence, and felt more strength than if he had rested for weeks. I hope you are getting my message. Relax, do not fear everything you do with pain. That thought alone will wear you out and take all your energy. You will be tired for days because of the *"what if"* fear. The problem of chronic emotional fatigue began with what if, what if, and what if!

A person who suffers from chronic emotional fatigue will have anxiety and panic that saps every drop of energy that they have. That is why I say challenge yourself daily. Women are especially bad. Her whole day is effort. She probably has to take children to school each morning, drive home, do the housework, wash, shop, pick up the children after school, cook dinner, bath the children and get them to bed. If you are reading this hoping that I have a magic bullet for you I must break the news, I do not! The only magic lies in your attitude toward the situation. Hard isn't it? You must be prepared to work slowly at a pace you can manage. If that means crawling, then you must crawl, and not blame yourself for working this way. Do not blame yourself because you are ill. You think you are letting the family down. Do not blame yourself if you leave the house untidy, or if the meals are not as satisfactory as you think they should be. Do not knock yourself too often for letting a neighbor pick up the children after school.

If you are like this woman, you should try to put yourself into neutral. Back off, relax, take time to *"Smell the Flowers."* Do not make demands on yourself. Go to your own corner of the world. It means setting no standards at this stage. Above all, you must go forward as willingly as you can manage. Willingness relieves tension and so relieves fatigue. And by willingly, I really mean willingly do everything, rest willingly, accept overtiredness willingly. If you cannot decide about how much you should do and seem to stand wondering, accept this willingly. Accept everything willingly, and stop fighting that unseen enemy. Above all, close the door on self-pity, and spoil yourself a little. In my first book, *The Anxiety Epidemic,* I call this *taking time to smell the flowers.* It is a good phrase, remember it. It means stealing a few minutes of enjoyment for yourself. Buy some books, some magazines and read them. If the clothes need ironing, allow yourself rest periods during the day. Even if the ceiling is cracking and threatens to fall, give yourself permission to relax a few minutes. When I am working hard, especially writing for hours, at the end of each hour, whether I am tired or not, I sit back for five minutes. I take several deep breaths and go to my little corner of the world. This stops my shoulders from aching. I get the rest in before the pain begins. Stay relaxed and more productive.

Many patients with chronic emotional fatigue ask if they should continue to work. My answer is yes. I feel you should work as long as possible rather than sitting at home idle and depressed. When you stay home, you loose the last remnant of confidence and feeling of belonging. If a person has to quit work, he joins the band of sufferers wondering how much they can do, if anything. In order for an emotionally fatigued person to continue to work, you must not punish yourself with feelings of being helpless, hopeless or memories of the past that bring on more fatigue. You must try to work to the best of your ability. If you wonder how much you can do, I would rather have you overdo it than underdo it.

There are many problems for a person with chronic fatigue, especially if you have an employer who does not understand or is not sensitive to the problem. Since no two people are alike, each must be advised individually. You and your employer should consider the work problems and levels of stress.

Emotional fatigue depends a great deal on just how sensitized a person's nerves are. To test yourself, try this experiment that should illustrate the meaning of sensitization. Gently tap a wooden table with your finger, and you will hear a dull sound. Then with the same force, tap the bottom of an empty pie pan. Notice the difference in sound. The sounding board, the wood and the empty pie tin differ, but not the strength of the tapping. Sensitized nerves make a very sensitive sounding board. There is nothing wrong with your nerves. They are simply responding to constant hammering by anxiety, tension, fear and uncertainty.

Sensitized nerves register emotion. They do so in an exaggerated way. This is difficult for an emotionally fatigued person to understand and deal with. He may feel a mild dislike transgressing into intolerance where a few minutes waiting seems like hours and soft music becomes loud noise. The simple tap of a spoon against a saucer can reverberate painfully on overly sensitized ears. He does not find movies relaxing, instead intolerable. A child's crying sends a chronic emotionally fatigued person searching for dark solitude. So oversensitized, the sight of someone they love will bring tears and a rare minute of joy may be felt hysterically. A person in this state feels buffeted by an unknown force as though he is swinging up and down on an emotional swing. Many patients feel they will never have energy and enjoy life with family and friends as they once did.

Living with exaggerated emotions requires much energy. Emotional reserves can eventually be so drained that the sufferer becomes apathetic, then depressed. It is not easy to understand that when you are apathetic. You may have little emotional reserve to handle ordinary everyday feelings. Many say they can no longer feel love for their spouse or family. They describe an empty spot where feelings used to be. Even interest in sex is diminished.

Although chronic emotional fatigue sufferers feel like this, they can always manage to find enough reserve to register anxiety, fear and panic. Chronic emotional fatigue is very bewildering. It can cut a hole right through the middle of your life. You can lose all hope and feel totally helpless. When you understand sensitization and the feeling it may bring, the myths begin to clear. Things have meaning. Fear and uncertainty are not your ruler.

Severe chronic emotional fatigue and depression go hand in hand. You should think of depression as depletion of the mind and body. Depression implies a downward direction, a depth out of which the depressed person must somehow drag himself. Most feel it is an endless struggle, but it does not have to be. Do not struggle to bring yourself up out of anything. Stop struggling. If you can clear yourself not only of depression, which is depletion, but of chronic fatigue. Stop struggling, and start healing. The healing will be gradual, but it will happen. Rushing around, trying to get yourself up out of depression can make you more tired and depleted. Going out, meeting people, keeping busy is very helpful. Too often, you feel better when you are out, and become depressed as soon as you see your home. You begin playing old tapes.

Please remember recovery from depletion is gradual. You have dipped deeply into emotional reserves. It will take time for these reserves to be replenished just as a wound takes time to heal. This means you must work with the feeling of depression. You must be prepared to take it with you even though it can press heavily on your heart, or feel like a load of lead in your lungs.

If your doctor suggests antidepressants, they are not an answer; they will not help. Tell your doctor you prefer using a natural alternative such as amino acids. Amino acids treat the problem, not just the symptoms. Orthomolecular therapists and doctors know how to treat chronic emotional fatigue. Your immune system must be restored and your brain chemistry put back into balance. I have devoted a complete section at the end of this book to help you with an orthomolecular approach.

Rosemary was a forty-three year old mother of two who had gone through a traumatic experience and had problems with depression. During one of our sessions she told me that some of her friends were trying to convince her that taking antidepressants was an answer. I told her no nervously ill person should be tied to taking antidepressants! I explained to her that a depressed chronically fatigued person would recover without antidepressants. I have never suggested them and all of my patients are doing well.

If you are willing to work on the understanding that feelings of depression are a form of depletion, the temporary symptoms will soon pass. Time and healing will gradually recharge your batteries, especially after the age of forty. Do not become impatient! Above all beware of another draining emotion, despair. Despair can carry your spirits down a doom and gloom cycle and prolong healing. I call these the draining three D's, depression, depletion and despair.

Jan, a thirty-six year old teacher suffering from chronic emotional fatigue, lost a close friend to cancer. She asked me what she should do about the funeral in her present state of mind. I advised her to do what she felt she could handle. The only expectations she had to live up to were her own. Emotional fatigue makes a person feel overwhelmed by even the smallest things, let alone cope with the death of a friend. She went to the funeral and sat in the back. She did not view her friend as she chose to remember her as she was when she was alive, not as she was in the coffin. Halfway through the service she left.

Later, Jan told me she felt like a failure. She was not a failure. She was only protecting her already oversensitized nervous system. Sometimes an incident of this nature can bring on feelings of guilt that can become very intense and deeply hurt the sensitized person that feels they will never recover. Feelings of guilt must be dealt with one at a time until they diminish. Be careful not to let guilt open old wounds because your mind and body have reached a point of saturation. Do not play old tapes!

Acceptance, obviously, may not carry you upwards, but it does stop you from sinking into despair. As I already mentioned, finding something interesting to do, especially with other people, does help. It is very difficult for a homemaker going through the daily chores to find interest. Her main hope is to accept depletion as willingly as she can. Working with it, knowing that if she does, it will also allow her to feel better sooner.

The third fatigue is mental fatigue. Constant, anxious, inward thinking in chronic emotional fatigue will bring brain drain that of course, is mental fatigue. Thoughts slow down and thinking becomes an effort. Instead of thoughts flitting lightly from subject to subject as they do when you are fresh. In a chronically, emotionally, drained person thoughts come with a great deal of effort. It is almost as if each thought has to be worked through twice. These sufferers become easily confused, finding concentration and remembering arduous. Talking to others becomes such a strain that when the chronically tired person sees a neighbor approaching, they cross to the other side of the street to avoid them. Similarly, they avoid answering the telephone like the plague. Before they were ill they could spend hours on the weekend sitting in the sun, lazily dipping into the newspaper, sometimes hardly thinking at all. While time spent now is watched minute by minute. Thoughts that come slowly seem difficult to discard. It is almost as if they stick in the mind.

This is one reason why a mentally tired person gnaws at a problem and seems unable to let it go. One woman said that although she knew she loved her husband, the thought that she did not, kept recurring. The thoughts were so convincing, she was beginning to think they must be true. I explained that the thoughts were convincing her because she was sensitized, and therefore, it made such a deep impression. I also explained that the thoughts kept returning because she was mentally tired.

When mental fatigue and sensitization work together, throwing off frightening ideas may seem impossible. Never be disturbed by this. Never fight to get rid of an unwanted thought. Let it come. Take it with you. Work with it. Resolve it or let it go. If you fight, you only add more tension, and you make the thought seem more important than it is. Once you make it important, it is much more difficult to forget. You should not try to forget it. You make it unimportant by taking it with you. See it for what it is, only a thought. Work with it. It will soon dissolve with time.

A patient admitted that the thought that she did not love her husband came most forcefully and clung most tenaciously when she was very tired. In addition, she said there were moments when she could see it for what it was, only a thought. Then it seemed so silly, and she could even smile at it.

I call this sudden fleeting ability to see distressing thoughts in true prospective, realistic observation. The mentally tired person may be able to observe the truth or even another acceptable point of view, perhaps only once or twice daily. But that brief observation is enough to show him the trick mental fatigue is playing on him. It is enough to encourage him not to take his upsetting ideas too seriously at this stage of his illness. Also, with mental tiredness, forgetting becomes such a habit, the sufferer may begin to believe that he is going prematurely senile. The nervously ill person's imagination is so fertile.

One woman said, "Doctor, you would not believe the terrible thoughts that keep bugging me, unreal thoughts."

Of course, I believed her. I have heard about such thoughts often. If you cannot remember, leave notes for yourself, and if you forget where you put the notes, see the humor in it. Does it matter so much whether you remember now? You remember only too easily when you are well. You remember things you would rather forget. Forgetting easily is all part of emotional fatigue. An anxious person worries continually about the state he is in. He gradually loses interest in other things, and the outside world may become unreal.

Feelings of unreality are what you make of them. They are always an offshoot of fear or anxious feelings. Feeling unreal does not mean you are going crazy. It does not mean you are permanently losing touch with the world. It means no more than you are being fearful about your illness for so long that thinking about it seems more natural at the moment than being drawn out of yourself to think about other things. Feel as unreal as your introspection demands. Do not be frightened by it. I promise you that when you begin to recover, other interests will return, and the feeling of unreality will fade.

Fatigue can accentuate unreality. Fatigue of the eye muscles can interfere with the functioning of the lens. Vision may seem blurred or you may have difficulty focusing. You may notice it more when looking quickly from a near object to a distant one or vice versa. Also, objects in bright sunlight may seem as if they are in a dark shadow. The sufferer may complain that everything suddenly goes dark. This can be fearful. But, it is only temporary. If you do not understand that this black world is caused by eye muscle fatigue, you panic. You add more stress and tension to your body so it takes longer for the world to return to its normal brightness.

Can you see how important understanding is? Ignorance of how fear and fatigue work can trick you into doing the wrong thing? Again, acceptance, staying in reality, floating, drifting and relaxing are the keys!

The fourth and last fatigue is fatigue of spirit. Talking about fatigue of the spirit is not very scientific, but I have no doubt you understand my meaning. Fatigue of the spirit means that the chronically fatigued person is beginning to feel that the struggle is becoming too much. You lose your will to go on struggling. It is as if your brain has been drained of vitality. Some say they feel a hundred years old and cannot bear the thought of looking at the future. Simply facing tomorrow seems almost beyond them.

If you have had only some of these experiences I have been talking about, do not immediately become upset and think, "Does all that have to happen to me?" It does not. By listening to what I have said, you will understand and have some idea of how to cope with emotional fatigue. The key to coping is stop struggling. When you struggle against the feelings, the symptoms of anxiety, fatigue or are struggling to avoid them, you become more tense, more fatigued, more sensitized and more anxious and fearful. So stop struggling. Give up the struggle. But it is not easy to stop struggling and go forward in to the uncertainty that the symptoms bring. It is not easy to work with an unknown future. It is not easy when your body feels as if it is vibrating, shaking, stomach churning, limbs aching, heart pounding, vision blurring, or head swimming. Thoughts perpetually revert to your illness. It is not easy when the mind feels as if it is drawn out into a thin thread that will snap at the slightest extra strain.

A mother loved her daughter dearly but dreaded her coming home on weekends. She shrank from the thought of having to take the extra strain of the daughter's critical gaze as she asked hopefully, "Are you any better, Mother?" That is not easy to take, but it is possible.

Recently a woman telephoned to say that the morning had been especially rough for her. But she came through it by saying to herself....I will be much better in an hour or so. I will listen to a relaxation tape and do slow, deep breathing until I feel relaxed and in control. I will have some peace then, and perhaps a little while afterwards. The thought of peace to come, sustained her. But while she lived for those peaceful moments, she made very little progress. I explained that true lasting peace did not lie in the moments of relief from suffering. These were only rest periods or intermissions. The real peace lay deep within her.

The peace would reflect in her attitudes at the time when she was feeling the dreaded sensations at their peak. That was the moment when she had to find real peace through acceptance of the symptoms by not struggling and being willing to work with her feelings. She thought for a while and then said, "You mean I have to find the eye of the hurricane." She had the right message at last. Sailors say that at the center of a hurricane there is a place of peace that they call the "eye" The storm swirls around it, but you cannot touch it. If you are to find it, you must first sail through the storm. If that woman would work as willingly as possible with the hurricane raging, she would find the eye of the storm within herself. She would have found real peace, although the symptoms were still present. True peace lies not in the absence of symptoms, but in their midst. It is not until you have found this peace that you will eventually find the other peace, the peace that comes when the symptoms have finally gone.

The next day the woman reported that while in pain, she sat at work. She was a writer and worked for two hours, and for the first time in years, was able to almost lose herself in the work while the hurricane raged. Somehow the hurricane did not seem so important. It takes courage to go into the storm. It is more usual to think that you must hold on. If you do not, the symptoms get worse. That woman had been holding on for years without relief. Is it not time she tried letting go? Try going into the storm willingly or as willingly as you can manage.

I want you to practice willingness and feel yourself stop struggling. In other words, feel acceptance. Take a deep breath, let it out slowly. Let your stomach muscles sag, give way, and try to get a feeling of willingness to accept what ever. As you relax, it will pass. However faint the feeling, relax through it. Go ahead, take a slow, deep breath. Did you feel a tiny feeling stir? If you did, you felt the birth of recovery. When you first learn how to accept, you have laid down the foundations. Continued acceptance finishes the job.

At first, you must be prepared for peace to come slowly, in patches. You may feel gloriously peaceful one day and in turmoil the next. In the peaceful moments you may think, "I'm cured." But let some new stress come and your nerves at this stage will continue to register stress too intensely. It takes time for sensitization to heal. Understand this, and never be discouraged by slow recovery in the early stages. Time, more time, is always the answer and give it willingly. You now have a key to understanding.

Suffering like yours, in many ways, is a privilege. We learn by contrast. Until we have known emotional pain, we will never know the true meaning of peace, and goodness knows, you have known pain. Later, when you read words like these, music is gentler on the spirit than tired eyelids upon tired eyes. They will mean something more to you than just beauty because you know how tired eyes can really be. Never begrudge what you have been through. Starting now, this very moment, not tomorrow, try your best to accept it all. Stop struggling. Do not fight anything. I promise that when you do this, you will gradually be your old self again, perhaps, a better self or at least, a more understanding self. Your energy will come back, and you will look forward to life again.

Chronic emotional fatigue attacks those who cannot express, sort out or deal with stress, anxiety, depression, fear or grief. Do not repress. Express. Declare yourself to those who are trying to take control of your life. I have found health, happiness and peace of mind are the keys to the best quality of life you could ever dream of. Peace be with you.

Special Note to Parents

Over the past several years in my work with hyperactive, A.D.D. children and teenagers with behavioral problems, I have noticed that many will display symptoms of chronic emotional fatigue. In many cases, the symptoms have been more pronounced after the child has gone through the death of a loved one, separation of parents or a traumatic episode. If your child is not one who verbalizes his feelings to you, and constantly tends to withdraw complaining that he feels tired all the time, be aware. You should have him checked by someone who understands chronic emotional fatigue. Do not be talked into antidepressants or quick fixes in psychiatric hospitals. They are never the answer, and the child will suffer from it for the rest of his life.

Dr. Doris Rapp, one of the world's foremost authorities in pediatric allergies in Buffalo, New York, has just released a book entitled, *Is This Your Child?* I strongly suggest if your child is having problems, you invest in this book. Dr. Rapp goes into great detail describing the Tension Allergic Fatigue Syndrome.

Another resource is my book entitled, *Controlling Hyperactivity With Amino Acids and Nutrients.*

Letting Go
A Guided Imagery

(To be read slowly to a friend or silently to oneself at least daily)

Direct your attention to your breathing.

Not the thought of the breathing, but the direct sensation of the breathing, as the air enters and leaves by itself.

Let the awareness come right to the edge of sensation as the breath enters and leaves the nostrils.

Let the awareness be soft and open, making contact with each breath without the least interference.

Experience the natural tides of the breath, as it comes and goes. Do not attempt to change or control it. Just observe it.

Open to receive each changing sensation that accompanies the breath, moment to moment.

Let the breath breathe itself, without comment or without any attempt to control it in anyway. Allow the breath to be as it is. If it is slow, let it be slow. If it is deep, let it be deep. If it is shallow, let it be shallow. Allow awareness and sensation to meet, moment to moment, with each inhalation and with each exhalation.

Let the breath be completely natural and free, in no way held by the mind. Just the breath breathing itself. Sensations arise, instant to instant, in the vast spaciousness of awareness.

If you notice the mind attempting to shape the breath, to control it in even the least way, just watch that tendency and let the breath float free. No holding. No control.

Completely let go of the breath. Let the body breath by itself. Do not interfere with the subtle flow. Just awareness as vast as the spacious sky.

The sensations of the breath, arise and pass away within this openness. Nothing to hold to. Nothing to do. Just the breath as it is.

Float, drift, relax and return whenever you want.

The Art of Feeling Good
Things to Know

1. When you feel you have a *negative* mood do not worry. It means feeling down or depressed. It is a sense of pessimism and unhappiness.

2. Some *negative* moods are normal and cannot be avoided totally.

3. *Negative* moods as with any mood can be changed. They are not permanent, even though you feel like it will last forever.

4. A *negative* mood is the result of illogical, irrational uncertainty in thinking.

5. *Negative* moods are changed by focusing on what you want to do, not what you have.

6. Focusing on and thinking about *negative* feelings does not change the feelings. You are playing old tapes in your mind.

7. Changing how you think (self-talk) and what you do (your behavior) will change your feelings. Control your life.

8. If you start to think negatively, stop and reverse the behavior pattern.

9. If you do not believe you can change your thoughts or behaviors, chances are your thoughts and behaviors will not change.

The Art of Feeling Good
Things to Do

You can change your moods and feel better without the use of prescription drugs. You have control over your thinking. If you feel your mood going downward, use a self talk approach as well as positive affirmation tapes.

When a *negative* mood occurs, identify what your negative thoughts are at that time. Does it follow a "stressful day?" Are you more fatigued? Do you feel helpless? Take control back. Rethink the *negative* mood, then take time to project yourself into a positive place.

If you leave out the positive, you fail to recognize and acknowledge the positive things that occur in your life. When you feel down, you tend to forget the positive events that have happened in your life.

The "what if" mood creates *negative* moods. Do not try to look into the future. Stay in the present. During a *negative* mood and when dwelling on the *negative* your mental filter tends to allow in only the dark, *negative* thoughts. You tend to focus upon those things that have not gone according to your plans.

Irrational beliefs like the ones above are the basis of *negative* moods. Follow this simple formula when *negative* moods occur:
- Ask yourself what are the thoughts that preceded the negative mood. If necessary, write down the thoughts.
- Determine what type of irrational thoughts you are thinking.
- Change your thinking (mental self talk) to combat and destroy your irrational or illogical thoughts. Tell yourself:
  - Not to overgeneralize.
  - Not to assume the worst.
  - To find the positive in your life.
  - To stop stomping on the positive.
  - Reinforce yourself, even if you do not think you deserve it. You do.

Symptoms of Chronic Emotional Fatigue

1. Anxiety
2. Mood swings
3. Mental and physical fatigue
4. Sluggishness
5. Chronic muscle spasms
6. Uncertainty
7. Fear that comes and goes
8. Panic attacks
9. Sleep problems
10. Chronic digestive upset
11. Constant body aches and pains
12. Stiff neck and / or limited range of motion
13. Muscle jerks
14. Churning stomach
15. Eye strain
16. Loss of interest
17. No sex drive
18. Pounding heart, skipped beats
19. Low self esteem
20. No confidence
21. Withdrawal
22. Sensitivity to bright lights
23. Sensitivity to noise, especially loud sounds
24. Depression
25. Tension headaches or other headaches.
26. Constant stress
27. Blurred vision
28. Constant fear of failure
29. Feelings of helplessness and hopelessness
30. Feelings of guilt
31. As fatigued in the morning upon awakening as when you
    went to bed.
32. Apathy
33. Tension

Causes and Symptoms of Stress

Stress is a subjective and personal effect. What is stressful to you may not be to someone else. People react differently to various situations. Just because something does not cause stress to others does not mean it might not be stressful to you. Stress triggers can come from a variety of sources including overwork, addiction in either yourself or a loved one, death of a loved one, divorce, lack of sleep, changes or loss of employment, increased use of tranquilizers, antidepressants or pain medications, unexpected illness or anything that taxes you mentally or physically. Both positive and negative stressors are taxing, even if a change is for the good. It may involve readjustments, uncertainty and anxiety. Other sources of stress might be negative thinking habits, a high-strung or impulsive character, emotional drains, social pressures, conflicts, confusion, frustration, loneliness and boredom. Even certain diseases, injuries, pain, chemical or radiation exposure, and drugs can be the catalyst for stress. The warning signal for danger comes when small stresses begin to combine, multiplying their effects, especially when they remain unresolved.

The Symptoms of Stress

Over the past ten years we have done extensive research at the Pain & Stress Center on the physical and mental effects of stress. Stress causes a slow deterioration of your immune system and your mental functioning. One day you just cannot seem to get it all together, and you are overwhelmed by fear and confusion which add to the effects of stress.

The first level of symptoms is very slight. Symptoms can be as mild as losing interest in doing enjoyable activities, consuming too much alcohol, sagging of the corners of the eyes. Additional symptoms include becoming short-tempered, being bored, nervousness, rolling of your hands or developing creases in your forehead. These are evidence that the brain and body are dealing with more than they can handle. *At this point you should stop and evaluate your lifestyle and see what changes you can make. Take control of your life.*

The second level of symptoms is more noticeable. Tiredness, angry outbursts, insomnia, loss of interest, fears, sadness, nagging anxiety, loss of sex drive, changes in eating habits, and withdrawal. These are important warning signs that you are not handling your stress. Changes should be made immediately to reverse the cycle. Evaluate your lifestyle, diet and nutrients. *If you cannot make the necessary changes, seek a therapist to help you.*

The third level of symptoms includes physical symptoms: headaches, neck and back pain, aches all over, muscle spasms, high blood pressure, crying, digestive problems, strange heartbeats, facial tics, never feeling well, constant anxiety and depression, inability to concentrate, use of antidepressants, pain medications, tranquilizers or daily alcohol ingestion. These signs are evidence that the stress is having a serious effect on your body and mind. *Immediate actions should be taken to make changes; get professional assistance.*

The fourth level of symptoms can result in actual disease such as heart disease, cancer, skin disorders, ulcers, asthma, stroke, hepatitis, kidney failure, chronic allergies, susceptibility to infection, chronic pain or mental breakdown. All of these have in many cases been related to prolonged stress.

Many times some diseases can be reversed by eliminating the stress, taking needed nutrients and amino acids or getting the right therapy. Sometimes they can be brought on by other factors but greatly aggravated by additional stress conditions. Often, even the condition itself creates additional stress, and therefore aggravates the condition.

Disease is now coming to be seen as arising from causes within the person such as nutrient imbalances and the body's reaction to environmental changes. People have begun to take direct responsibility for their health. Our interest in nutrition is a symbol of this health change of attitude. The functions of amino acids are the most diverse of any of the nutrient groups. They contribute to the formation of proteins, muscles and neurotransmitters which is the chemical language of the brain. Stress demands more amino acids because they are burned so rapidly.

When you repress or suppress

those things which you

don't want to live with . . .

you don't really solve the

problem because you

don't bury the problem

dead - you bury it

alive - it remains

alive and active

inside of you.

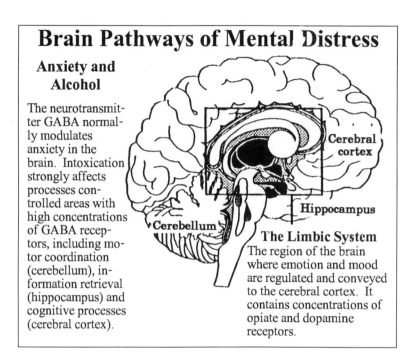

Brain Pathways of Mental Distress

Anxiety and Alcohol

The neurotransmitter GABA normally modulates anxiety in the brain. Intoxication strongly affects processes controlled areas with high concentrations of GABA receptors, including motor coordination (cerebellum), information retrieval (hippocampus) and cognitive processes (cerebral cortex).

Cerebral cortex

Hippocampus

Cerebellum

The Limbic System
The region of the brain where emotion and mood are regulated and conveyed to the cerebral cortex. It contains concentrations of opiate and dopamine receptors.

Chronic emotional fatigue depletes the brain of amino acids which are the precursors to inhibitory neurotransmitters in the brain. The neurotransmitters are the chemical language of the brain. The amino acids, GABA, glycine, tyrosine, taurine and tryptophan are very important to those who suffer chronic emotional fatigue and should be taken on a daily basis. GABA and glycine are for anxiety. Tyrosine is for depression. Taurine is for the skeletal muscle and central nervous system. Tryptophan is for sleep. Until tryptophan is available, melatonin will be helpful for restful sleep. Amino acids are an extremely important part of the healing process.

Charting the Brain's Activities

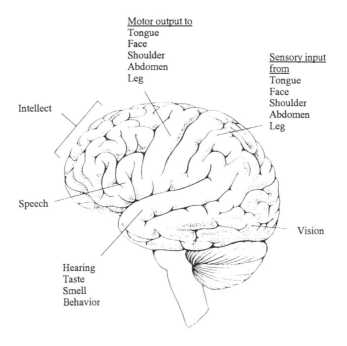

Motor output to
Tongue
Face
Shoulder
Abdomen
Leg

Sensory input from
Tongue
Face
Shoulder
Abdomen
Leg

Intellect

Speech

Hearing
Taste
Smell
Behavior

Vision

Each area of the brain regulates particular activities. Generally, the inner structures control basic metabolic processes, while the outer and front areas serve more advanced functions. Each side of the brain receives the sensory impressions and mobilizes the muscles of the opposite side of the body.

Stress can be analyzed into several levels, regardless of the stress source. As stress increases, the total caloric needs go up primarily because protein calorie needs increase. Thirty percent of the diet ideally should be amino acids. When the body is under severe stress, protein is broken down first.

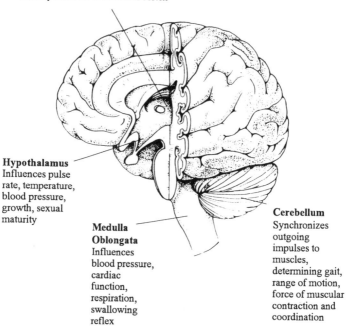

Thalamus
Takes in conscious sensory stimuli (excluding taste) and transfers them to specialized sensory areas on the cerebral cortex

Hypothalamus
Influences pulse rate, temperature, blood pressure, growth, sexual maturity

Medulla Oblongata
Influences blood pressure, cardiac function, respiration, swallowing reflex

Cerebellum
Synchronizes outgoing impulses to muscles, determining gait, range of motion, force of muscular contraction and coordination

Amino acids in combination with magnesium, B6 and other nutrients supports proper brain function. Chronic emotional fatigue depletes nutrients and weakens the immune system. The effect of stress on the immunity is complex. It combines several mechanisms including other hormones and body chemicals from the thyroid gland, sex glands and brain.

Behavior Cycle

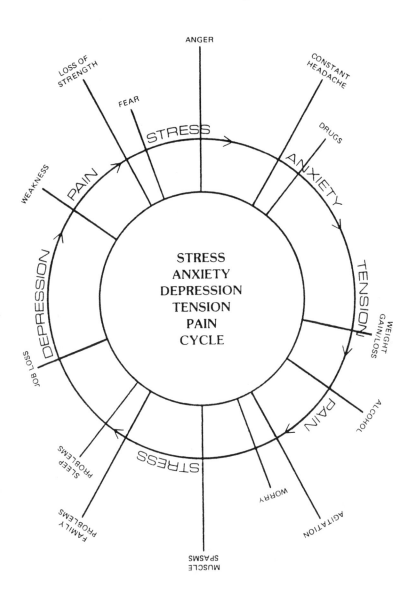

Nutritional Support Program for Chronic Emotional Fatigue

Your diet should be one of your first considerations. Your diet should be low in fat and simple carbohydrates, moderate in protein intake, and high in fiber. Become a label reader. There are many hidden substances that are usually high in fat and sugar in many processed foods. Become an informed consumer.

A "cave man" diet is generally a good diet. This diet basically is high in fruits and vegetables, low in fat, moderate in proteins. The foods are generally eaten without a great deal of preparation and in a more whole form. As an example, a baked potato is preferred over mashed or fried potatoes. The baked potato is higher in fiber and is also high in complex carbohydrates. Simple carbohydrates such as sugar should be avoided. Simple carbohydrates raise your blood sugar rapidly giving you a false high. But this only lasts for a short time before your blood sugar plummets and you hit bottom. If sugar is your downfall, try using some of the recipes in *Breaking Your Sugar Addiction Cookbook* by Kathy Birkner for some alternative ideas that are good and quick to prepare

Do not eat fried foods as your body has to work much harder to overcome the free radicals created. Fried foods equal high fat content. Limit the amount of fat you ingest. Stay with chicken, turkey or fish, while only occasionally eating beef.

Limit your intake of caffeine. Caffeine has been linked to increased anxiety and nervousness. Do not forget that most regular sodas are high in sugar and contain caffeine. Instead try some water or herbal teas for a change.

Limit your ingestion of alcohol. Alcohol tends to be high in sugar. Again, it may relax you, but it can also backfire causing depression and anxiety, and it is habit forming. It can also cause havoc with your sinuses and allergies, and further zap your energy.

Avoid smoking or smoke. Even inhalation of second-hand smoke can cause problems with your energy level and contributes to free radicals in your body. Avoid it like the plague!

Consider food allergies if you have either environmental or airborne allergies or you have problems with your sinuses. Food allergies can be a source of many underlying problems such as fatigue and lack of energy.

The following is the supplementation program used at the Pain & Stress Therapy Center for patients with chronic emotional fatigue. All patients have shown a marked improvement using this program.

1. **Good Mulit-Vitamin** such as Total Vites.

2. **Liquid Magnesium** - 1/2 to 1 teaspoon two to three times per day in juice. One of the most common symptoms of magnesium deficiency are chronic neck, back, and shoulder pains with recurrent muscle spasms. Muscles cannot relax without magnesium. If you have constant muscle spasms, migraines, depression, exhaustion, arrythmias, twitches or tremors, you are probably magnesium deficient. Other symptoms besides chronic pain that are often helped or relieved by magnesium are anxiety and pain, nervousness, cold white fingers, insomnia, hypertension, excessive perspiration and body odor and irregular heartbeats.

Over the past year, I had the opportunity to listen to Sherry Rogers, M.D. She has done more research on magnesium and magnesium deficiencies than anyone in the U.S. Dr. Rogers reports excellent results with her patients that had described the above symptoms using magnesium therapy.

3. **Tyrosine** (1000 to 1700 mg per day in divided doses). Tyrosine is available in 500 and 850 mg capsules. Dosage depends on a person's weight. This aids in restoring the brain chemistry from stress exhaustion. Tyrosine enhances neurotransmitters and aids in lifting the symptoms of depression. Phenylalanine breaks down to tyrosine in the liver. Tyrosine is converted to dopa, then epinephrine and norepinephrine. Most antidepressants work by increasing or manipulating the amount of norepinephrine in the brain. Tyrosine does this naturally whereas most drugs have side

effects. A word of warning, if you are taking antidepressants, you cannot just stop taking them and start taking tyrosine. Tyrosine or phenylalanine CANNOT be combined with tricyclic antidepressants or MAO inhibitors. Check with your pharmacist or physician.

4. **Melatonin** - 1 at bedtime. The pineal gland through its production of melatonin serves as a critical link between the brain and the immune system. A number of studies show that melatonin elevates the activity of certain types of immune system cells that are important in fighting infections. It is especially effective in restoring the defenses of a person whose immune system has been weakened by stress according to *Longevity,* October, 1990.

5. **Esterified Vitamin C** -5 to 25,000 mg per day in divided doses. Esterified C is a vitamin C that has a neutral pH or the same as distilled water. It does not cause the side effects often associated with large amounts of ascorbic acid. Esterified C forms a metabolite with the body so if you took a dose now, twenty-four hours later, some of the C would still be present in your body. Vitamin C is important for the repair of body tissues and helps fight infections.

6. **Reishi mushroom** capsules or tablets- 4 to 8 per day in divided doses. In the Orient Reishi is a highly esteemed herb that has been touted for longevity, energy and health. Studies by Dr. William Stavinoha, a pharmacologist at the University of Texas Health Science Center in San Antonio show that Reishi has great anti-inflammatory effects. One tablet or capsule is equivalent to 5 mg hydrocortisone. Note: Not all Reishi is created equal. Some brands of Reishi are made from Reishi mycelium mixed with grain. This Reishi mycelium does not contain the full complement of compounds. Only mature Reishi mushrooms provide the full spectrum of compounds that have been prized in traditional Chinese and Japanese herbology for hundreds of years.

7. **Glutamine** 1000 mg daily if you are having problems concentrating or remembering.

8. **Chromium picolinate** - 1 to 2 (200 mcg) caps per day. Chromium is a trace mineral that is extremely important in blood sugar utilization and regulation working with insulin. In addition,

chromium assists in fat metabolism and plays a part in cholesterol and fat levels in the body. Chromium helps to regulate blood sugar and sugar cravings.

9. **Lysine** - 1000 to 1500 mg per day for skin problems or herpes.

10. **CoEnzyme Q10** -30 to 60 mg per day. CoQ10 is a natural nutrient essential to the life and health of every cell. You cannot fight off infections without CoQ10 which decreases with age. Research indicates CoQ10 plays a critical role in the production of energy in almost every cell in the body, and may play a major role in the treatment and prevention of serious diseases.

11. **DLPA (DL-Phenylalanine)** 750 mg capsules - 2 to 6 per day in divided doses. DLPA is an amino acid that has been helpful for pain and depression. DLPA is not habit forming and works with other nutrients to reduce pain. Again, if you are taking antidepressants make sure that this does not conflict with your medication.

12. **Boswella** 150 mg capsule- 2 twice per day with food. The herb, Boswella, comes from India. It has anti-inflammatory properties and has been used for pain in Aryuvedic medicine. When selecting boswella be sure the brand you chose is pure pharmaceutical grade boswella with no fillers.

13. **Fortified Flax** - 1 to 2 teaspoons twice a day. This can be added to fruit juice or sprinkled over salad or cereal. Flax provides Omega 3 oil which is the "good" oil or fat for the body. Flax helps support the immune system and is extremely high in fiber.

14. **Scavenger Antioxidant Formula**- 2 to 3 per day. Scavengers are a combination of beta-carotene, Vitamin C, bioflavonoids, Rutin, Vitamin E, selenium, cysteine, and B6 or P 5' P. Free radicals attack cell components and damage cells and tissues of the body. Over time, these free radicals are at the root of may diseases and aging processes. Free radicals are a group of highly reactive substances called oxidants. Free radicals are unavoidable. They are formed during normal metabolic processes which occur in the body. They are also consumed in some foods, inhaled in air pollution and tobacco smoke. Additionally, they are generated in

the environment from radiation and herbicides. The scavenger group of vitamins helps to intercede, deactivate and render free radicals harmless before they cause irreversible damage to the body's tissues.

15. **Neurotransmitter Formula,** AM-PM Plus 2 three times daily and 2 at bedtime, if needed. This special combination of amino acids activates the neurotransmitters in the brain which help to restore brain chemistry to its natural state.

GABA is an inhibitory neurotransmitter in the brain that slows down the transmission of anxiety signals from the limbic system to the cortex or the thinking part of the brain. Many tranquilizers merely attach to the GABA receptor sites. GABA fills them. Stress depletes the levels causing increased symptoms of anxiety.

16. **B Complex Capsule** - 1 twice per day. The "B" vitamins are some of the most important stress fighting vitamins. Some, such as B6, are required to activate many metabolic processes in the body and are necessary to activate amino acids.

17. **Malic Acid** - 1 (600 mg) twice per day. It is my opinion that 95% of those who suffer chronic emotional fatigue are deficient in malic acid. I personally take 2 malic acid daily for reoccurring muscle spasms and tension in my shoulders. Within 48 hours after starting malic acid and Slow Mag, I could tell the difference. Malic acid is extracted from apples and is an important component in the formation of ATP production in the body. Malic acid is important in the Kreb Cycle, where fats and sugar are converted to energy. It offers relief for those who suffer from fibromyalgia or fibrositis. This chronic disorder causes pain and stiffness through the tissues that support and move bone and joints. Pain and localized tender points occur in the muscles, particularly those that support the neck, spine, shoulders and hips. Fatigue is a commonly associated problem. Latest figures show 3 to 6 million people in the U.S. or about 5% of the population suffer from fibromyalgia. Studies reported in the *Journal of Nutritional Medicine* that combining malic acid and Slow Mag give relief to this painful condition. Magnesium is also needed in this cycle.

18. **Power Plex** - 1 scoop twice per day in juice. Power Plex is a combination formula which provides amino acids, vitamins and

minerals to enhance energy levels, promote stamina and accelerates restoration after exercising.

19. **Alka Seltzer Gold** - Use as needed to help stop food intolerances or reactions. Recent studies show intolerance to food contributes to increased symptoms. Utilizing the food elimination or rotation diet helps to decrease food reactions and symptoms.

Self Help

A Directory of Orthomolecular Physicians and Therapists for U.S. is available. The list contains over 1000 names in various specialties. The list is available for $7.95

If you are unable to find help in your area, telephone consultations with Dr. Sahley or Dr. Birkner can be arranged by appointment. Please contact the office at (210) 614-7246 for information or an appointment during office hours (Monday - Thursday 9 A.M. to 5 P.M. and Friday 9 A.M.- 4 P.M. Central Time).

--------------------To Order --------------

Please Print

Name _____

Address _____

City _____ State _____ Zip _____

I would like to purchase	Price	Quantity	Total
Chronic Emotional Fatigue book	$3.95	_____	_____
The Anxiety Epidemic book (Dr. B.J. Sahley)	$9.95	_____	_____
Breaking Your Addiction Habit book (Drs. B.J. Sahley and K.Birkner)	$8.95	_____	_____
The Natural Way To Control Hyperactivity With Amino Acids and Nutrients (Dr. B.J. Sahley)	$6.95	_____	_____
Breaking the Sugar Addiction Cookbook (Kathy Birkner, C.R.N.A, Ph.D.)	$5.95	_____	_____
Anxiety Audio Cassette Tape (Dr. B.J. Sahley)	$10	_____	_____
Fear Audio Cassette Tape (Dr. B.J. Sahley)	$10	_____	_____
Phobias Audio Cassette Tape (Dr. B.J. Sahley)	$10	_____	_____
Anxiety / Panic Attacks Causes & Control Audio Cassette Tape (Dr. B.J. Sahley)	$10	_____	_____
Hyperactivity Causes & Control Audio Cassette Tape (Dr. B.J. Sahley)	$10	_____	_____
Communication Audio Cassette Tape (Dr. B. Sahley)	$10	_____	_____
Letting Go Audio Cassette Tape (Dr. B.J. Sahley)	$10	_____	_____
Guilt Audio Cassette Tape (Dr. B.J. Sahley)	$10	_____	_____
Being, Your Way Audio Cassette Tape (Dr. B. Sahley)	$10	_____	_____
Depression Audio Cassette Tape (Dr. B.J. Sahley)	$10	_____	_____
Anger Audio Cassette Tape (Dr. B.J. Sahley)	$10	_____	_____
Forgiving and Healing Audio Cassette Tape (Dr. Sahley)	$10	_____	_____
Escape Audio Cassette Tape (Dr. B.J. Sahley)	$10	_____	_____
Orthomolecular Directory of Physicians and Therapists	$7.95	_____	_____

SUBTOTAL _____

Texas Residents Add 7.75 % Sales Tax _____

**SHIPPING $3 first item and $0.75 subsequent _____

TOTAL _____

Send To: Pain & Stress Therapy Center
5282 Medical Drive, Suite 160, San Antonio, TX 78229

**Canadian & Other Foreign Countries ADD $5 to the above amounts. We accept U. S. World Money Orders or MC / Visa / Discover ONLY!

Other Resources

As Someone Dies by Elizabeth A. Johnson

Allergies & Your Family by Doris Rapp, M.D.

The Anxiety Epidemic by Billie J. Sahley, Ph.D.

Breaking Your Addiction Habit by Billie J. Sahley

The E.I. Syndrome by Sherry Rogers, M.D.

The Great Anxiety Escape by Max Ricketts

Healing Images Audio Cassette by Bernie Seigal, M.D.

Mind as Healer, Mind as Slayer, Kenneth Pelletier, Ph.D.

The Melatonin Report by Billie J. Sahley, Ph.D.

Overcoming Fear Audio Cassette by Louise Hay

Thorson's Guide To Amino Acids by Leon Chaitow, D.O.

Tired or Toxic by Sherry Rogers, M.D.

The Way Up From Down by Priscilla Slagle, M.D.

52 Minutes To Turning Your Life Around Audio Cassette by
    David Viscott, M.D.

About the Authors

Billie J. Sahley, Ph.D., is Executive Director of the Pain & Stress Therapy Center in San Antonio. She is Board Certified Medical Psychotherapist and Orthomolecular Therapist. She is a Diplomate in the American Academy of Pain Management. Dr. Sahley is a graduate of the University of Texas, Clayton University School of Behavioral Medicine, and U.C.L.A. School of Integral Medicine. Additionally, she has studied advanced nutritional biochemistry through Jeffrey Bland, Ph.D. and HealthComm. She is a member of the Huxley Foundation, Academy of Psychosomatic Medicine, American Academy of Pain Management, Sports Medicine Foundation, American Association of Hyponotherapists and American Mental Health Counselors Association. Dr. Sahley is also on the Scientific and Medical Advisory Board for Inter-Cal Corporation. She is author of *The Anxiety Epidemic, Natural Way to Control Hyperactivity,* co-author of *Breaking Your Addiction Habit.*

Kathy Birkner is a C.R.N.A., Pain Therapist at the Pain & Stress Therapy Center in San Antonio. She is a Registered Nurse, Certified Registered Nurse Anesthetist, Texas Registered Massage Therapist and Orthomolecular Therapist. She is a Diplomate in the American Academy of Pain Management. She attended Brackenridge Hospital School of Nursing, University of Texas at Austin, Southwest Missouri State University and Clayton University. She holds degrees in nursing, nutrition and behavior therapy. Dr. Birkner has done graduate studies through the Center for Integral Medicine and U.C.L.A. Medical School under the direction of Dr. David Bresler. Additionally, she has studied advanced nutritional biochemistry through Jeffrey Bland, Ph.D. and Health-Comm. She is a member of the American Association of Nurse Anesthetists, Texas Association of Nurse Anesthetists, American Academy of Pain Management, American Professional Massage Therapists and Body-workers Association. Dr. Birkner is author of *Breaking Your Sugar Habit Cookbook* and co-author of *Breaking Your Addiction Habit.*